THE
CHRISTOPHER NORTON
ROCK PRELUDES
COLLECTION

BOOSEY & HAWKES

Boosey & Hawkes Music Publishers Ltd
www.boosey.com

CHRISTOPHER NORTON

Christopher Norton was born in New Zealand in 1953. After graduating he began his career as a teacher, pianist and composer, and began to develop an interest in popular music. Coming to the UK in 1977 on a university scholarship, he studied composition at York University with Wilfred Mellers and David Blake. Well established as a composer, producer, arranger and educationalist, Norton has written stage musicals, ballet scores, piano music, popular songs and orchestral music as well as jingles and signature tunes for TV and radio. He has lectured all over the world on aspects of his work and likes to integrate traditional teaching methods with aspects of modern technology.

Chris is best known for his world-famous series *Microjazz* — easy graded pieces in modern styles such as blues, rock 'n' roll, reggae and jazz — and for his award-winning *Essential Guides* to Pop Styles, Latin Styles and Jazz Styles.

www.christophernorton.com

NICOLA MELVILLE

Pianist Nicola Melville has commissioned and premiered many works by composers in the United States and her native New Zealand. She has recorded the complete piano rags of William Albright for the Equilibrium label. Her most recent CD, released on Innova Recordings, features thirteen new commissions by award-winning composers from around the US, and is available online. As well as being an advocate for new music, her ongoing interests include interdisciplinary performances that combine music with other arts in live performance.

Published by Boosey & Hawkes Music Publishers Ltd
Aldwych House
71–91 Aldwych
London
WC2B 4HN

www.boosey.com

AN IMAGEM COMPANY

ISMN 979-0-060-11638-4
ISBN 978-0-85162-475-4

First published 2005. Fifth impression 2013, with composer's corrections.

Printed in England by The Halstan Printing Group, Amersham, Bucks

Cover design by RF Design (UK) Limited
Nicola Melville recordings engineered, mixed and mastered by John Scherf
Band recordings by CN Productions

The original editions of *Rock Preludes* were dedicated to Barry Margan and Richard Mackie

THE
CHRISTOPHER NORTON
ROCK PRELUDES
COLLECTION

FULL PERFORMANCE & BACKING TRACK CD

 Solo piano tracks performed by Nicola Melville
Track numbers are shown in black circles

 Band demonstration tracks
Track numbers are shown in white circles.

 Band backing tracks
Track numbers are shown in grey circles.

WILDCAT

Rock Preludes 1 | *Prelude 1*

CHRISTOPHER NORTON

BLURRED HORIZON

Rock Preludes 1 | *Prelude 2*

CHRISTOPHER NORTON

Play last bar about 4 times,
gradually fading out & getting slower

JINGO

Rock Preludes 1 | *Prelude 3*

CHRISTOPHER NORTON

SIERRA

Rock Preludes 1 | *Prelude 4*

CHRISTOPHER NORTON

RISING FORCE

Rock Preludes 1 | *Prelude 5*

CHRISTOPHER NORTON

Molto allegro ♩ = c. 92

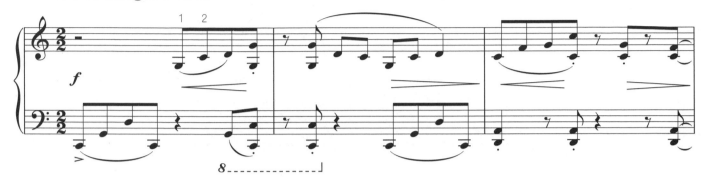

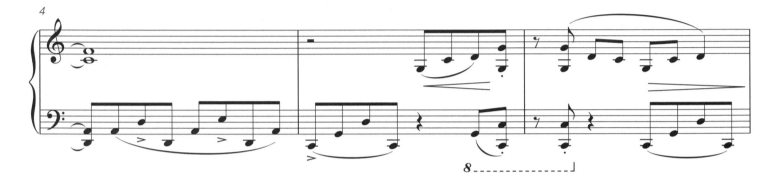

BLUE SNEAKERS

Rock Preludes 1 | *Prelude 6*

CHRISTOPHER NORTON

SUNSHINE PIECE

Rock Preludes 1 | *Prelude 7*

CHRISTOPHER NORTON

STURDY BUILD

Rock Preludes 2 | *Prelude 1*

CHRISTOPHER NORTON

Sternly ♩ = 132

COUNTRY SONG

Rock Preludes 2 | *Prelude 2*

CHRISTOPHER NORTON

Flowing ♩ = 132

FOUR, THREE

Rock Preludes 2 | *Prelude 3*

CHRISTOPHER NORTON

28

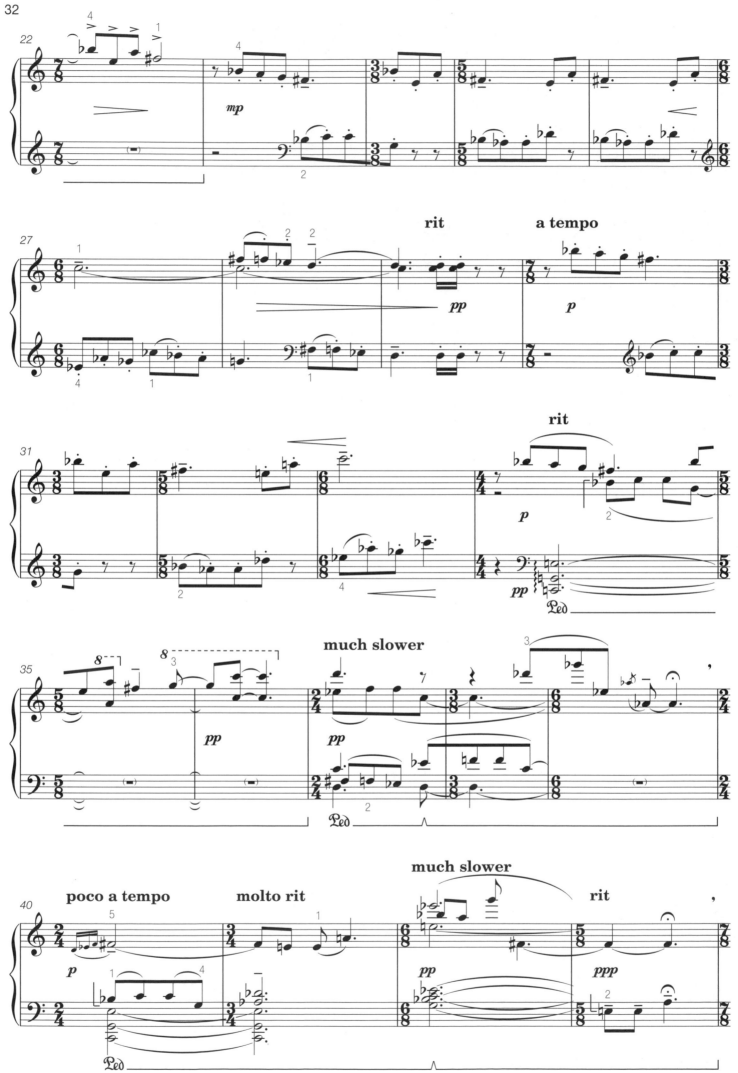

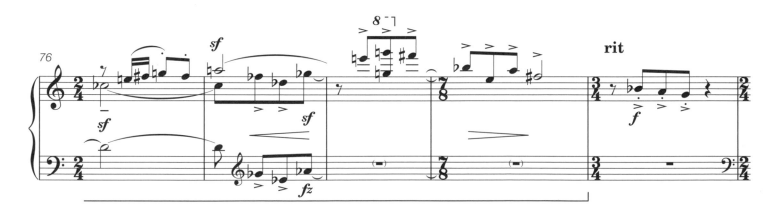

DREAMING ON

Rock Preludes 2 | *Prelude 4*

CHRISTOPHER NORTON

A STEADY HAND

Rock Preludes 2 | *Prelude 5*

CHRISTOPHER NORTON

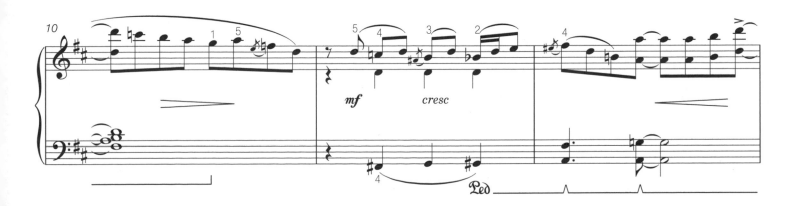

BARNYARD BLUES

Rock Preludes 2 | *Prelude 6*

CHRISTOPHER NORTON

FORCING THE PACE

Rock Preludes 2 | *Prelude 7*

CHRISTOPHER NORTON

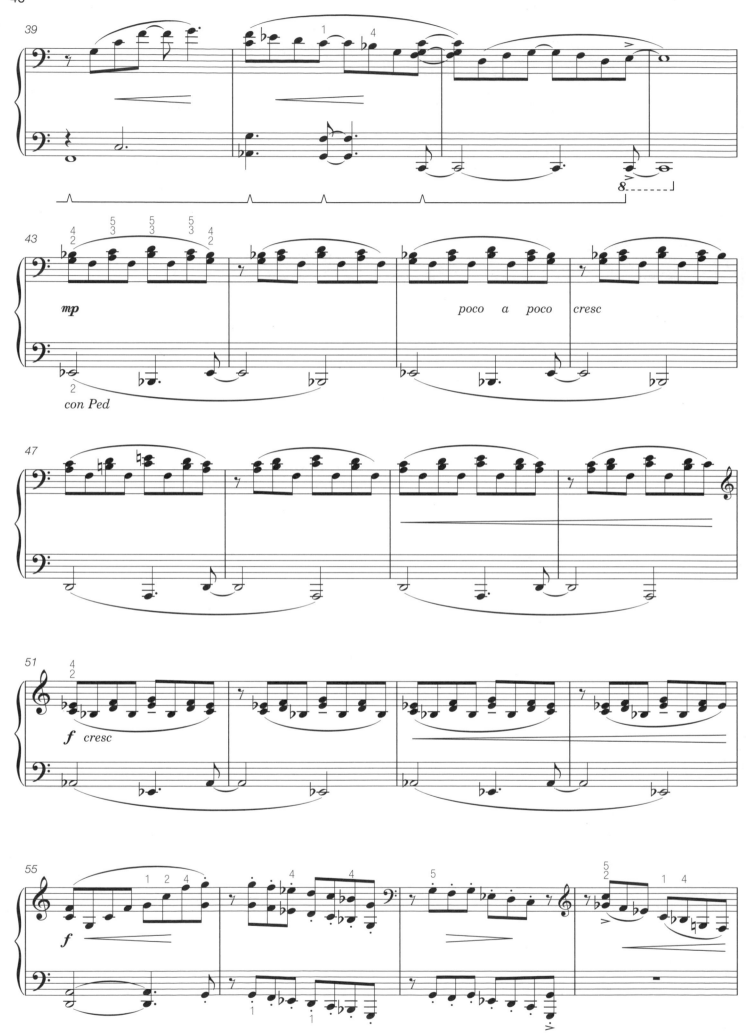